Po

Oats and Their Many Benefits

MARGARET BRIGGS

Abbeydale Press

ISBN: 978-1-86147-309-7

Published by ABBEYDALE PRESS
An imprint of Bookmart Ltd
Registered number 2372865
Trading as Bookmart Ltd
Blaby Road, Wigston
Leicester LE18 4SE

Production by Omnipress Limited, Eastbourne

Printed in Singapore

CONTENTS

INTRODUCTION

I hadn't realised before I started compiling this book
how emotive an object a bowl of porridge could be.
Who could imagine that a few basic ingredients could
create such cultural differences; who could foretell that
there are so many ways of preparing a humble, or not so
humble breakfast? Everyone I mention porridge to has a
very firm view on the product: you either love it or hate
the stuff.

I've vaguely known about the properties of oatmeal in
connection with face packs from my teenage years, but
the width and depth of beauty treatments made possible
by the inclusion of oats is quite staggering. Festivals and
events are held worldwide in the pursuit of the perfect
bowl of porridge, and rather than lose momentum over
the years have actually gained a new impetus.

The heralding of porridge oats as a major health food
and the introduction of the Glycaemic Index have added

weight to the health benefits of getting back to basic, wholegrain recipes. Celebrity consumers and chefs are constantly singing its praises. Throughout history, armies have marched on it and multitudes have slept on it or fed their horses on it.

There are countless references in literature to porridge, although some of the language it invokes does have the air of a porringer full of overcooked oats. Maybe some of the authors were not aware of the origins of sowing wild oats, or were not 'getting their oats'.

This book sets out to pull together a number of facts, some whimsical, some deadly serious, about oats. It gives helpful suggestions as to how best to consume them, whether with whipped cream, salt, butter, snails or any ingredient of your choice; whatever grabs you.

Best thing since sliced porridge!

KNOW YOUR OATS

Oats are produced from edible, starchy grains from the oat plant *Avena Sativa*, not to be confused with oat grasses. *Arrhenatherum* includes six species of tall grasses which are native to Europe and Asia and have been used as pasture grasses for animal grazing. *Danthonia* is a group of 100 species, all native to the southern hemisphere; they are particularly prolific in Australia, New Zealand and South American countries. In Australia oat grass is known as wallaby grass. Unfortunately, you wouldn't make much of a porridge from these plants.

Oats are annual plants which grow, flower and seed before dying in the autumn. The word 'oat' refers to both the plant and the grain. The exact number of species of *Avena Sativa* is unknown, but is estimated to be fewer than 50. The porridge oats we eat today were first found in western Europe as wild oats, or a weed growing with barley. The usefulness of these cereals for both human and animal foodstuffs quickly became apparent and oats spread around the world. Now known as common oats, they grow in cool temperate climates.

Red oats, originating in the Mediterranean region, are more heat tolerant and are grown in warmer climates. Wild red oats are considered to be weeds in most grain producing countries, but their properties, including resistance to rust spores and high yields, make them valuable plants for producing hybrid varieties.

SCATTER!

The problem with wild oats is that the seeds ripen quickly and scatter from the parent plant before harvesting is possible. This is an obvious disadvantage for farmers, and may give us a clue as to the origin of the expression 'sowing one's wild oats'. Oats have an awn, which is a long bristle-like tail at the tip of the lowest bract underneath the flower. The awn's function is to help the seed to plant itself. The wild red has a different awn from other varieties and twists with changing conditions, depending on weather conditions and humidity.

NO FLIES ON AVENA!

The movement of the awn pushes the seed into the ground to anchor it in the soil. This twisting reverses in dry weather so that the awn can untwist and revert to its original mode. Fishermen soon noticed this unique property and began to make flies from one or two awns tied together. Thus the 'fly' attracts fish, as it mimics the movements of insects landing on the water.

Avena Sativa has a flowering and fruiting structure made up of a number of branches bearing florets. These produce the caryopsis, or one-seeded fruits, of whose aphrodisiac qualities you will read more later!

WHO NEEDS THEM?

Oats are not classified as demanding plants and are second only to rye in their ability to adapt and survive in poor soil structures. They compete well with other cereals in poor soils and in short wet growing seasons. They will grow in sandy soils, highly acidic soils or any which are generally low in fertility. Areas of greatest production are concentrated in Europe, particularly in Sweden, Finland, Russia, Poland and Germany, and also in the USA, Canada and Australia. Canadian production remains fairly high.

HARVEST FOR THE WORLD?

World oats production in 2002/03 of 26.7 million tons compared with 27 million a year earlier and an average of about 30 million metric tons in the mid-1990s. Globally, average yields show wide divergence, from as low as less than 1.5 tons per acre at times in Russia and China to almost 5 tons per acre in Western Europe, notably in France. Russia remains one of the largest producers with about 8.2 million tons in 2002/03, nearly a third of the world's total, owing to the large acreage they are able to devote to oats. Among the few major producers Canada has shown relative steadiness in production during the past decade, averaging about 3.2 million tons, although lower yields in 2002/03 dropped production to about 2.9 million tons.

As world oat production has halved in the last 30 years, it now stands at about 25 million tons. Over this same period, world production of all grains has doubled at the expense of oats, which have tended to be squeezed out of crop rotations by other, higher yielding cereal crops. Most of the world's oat production is consumed domestically and world trade is small. In 2002/03 exports were forecast at 2.23 million tons vs. 1.83 million in 2001/02, with Canada accounting for almost half the total, namely 950,000 tons. Importing nations are more numerous, but the U.S. is the consistent leader with 1.75 million tons in 2002/03 vs. 1.4 million in 2001/02.

HAY FOR HORSES

In many countries the grains are used mainly as livestock feed, either in pure or mixed form. Oats provide straw for animal bedding and good hay, grazing and silage. One of the upward turns in the oat's markets is attributable to the niche market of horse feed. Although there are far fewer working horses around in the developed world than in previous centuries, keeping horses for recreational use has increased rapidly, to compensate for the market in preferred feed for horses and ponies, especially in the USA.

P FOR PORRIDGE

In other parts of the world oats are grown on a small scale for human consumption, especially as breakfast cereal. The pattern is constantly changing, and although there has been a decline in oat production for many years, the trend has changed again more recently, due to recognition of the various health benefits to be gained from eating porridge. In the UK 40% of the oats consumed find their way into porridge and oatmeal products. Oat grains are high in fibre and carbohydrates and contain 13% protein and only 6.9% fat. They are a source of calcium, iron, vitamin B and nicotinic acid. More recent figures show that the downward trend in European oat production has been reversed, with Sweden and Finland providing 40% of Europe's crop. Human consumption is on the increase in other parts of northern Europe as well, so perhaps the trend will grow and I'll be able to buy oats in south west France soon!

INDUSTRIAL APPLICATIONS

Another, less well known use of oat hulls is as a source of furfural, a chemical used in the production of various types of oily solvents. The dried hulls are rich in carbon sugars. Furfural is used in the refining of lubricating oils, in the manufacture of shoe dyes, herbicides and fungicides, and in the production of nylon.

Oat flour is used as a preservative on the inner coatings of paper bags for salted peanuts, coffee and crisps. It contains antioxidants which prevent fat-containing foods, such as peanut butter, margarine, chocolate and doughnuts from going rancid. Oat flour also stabilises fats in ice cream and other dairy products. If reconstituted with water, oat flour forms a gel for use in salad dressings, gravies, dips, soups, coatings and drink mixes. These gels can also replace fat in baked products.

OATS, GROATS, FLAKES AND BRAN

Groats are unflattened kernels with their husks or hulls removed. *Oatmeal* is made by grinding groats into pieces of varying texture from coarse to fine. Rolled oats are produced by steaming and flattening the kernels and removing the husks to make oatmeal. Rolled oats cook faster than steel-cut oats and are better for modern porridge making. *Oat flour* is unsuitable for making bread, but is used to make biscuits and puddings. *Steel-cut oats* have a dense and chewy texture, produced by running the grain through steel blades which slice them thinly.

Oats contain 70–75 percent groat, which is milled into steel-cut oats, rolled flakes, instant flakes, flour and bran. The remaining hull is waste, but can be burned for energy.

Much of early man's nutrition came from grain which had a tightly fitting husk. The only way to remove it was to burn it off. The resulting toasted grain had much better storage qualities than untoasted grains.

Naked oats have been developed which have a loose hull that is blown away during combining. The crude protein, oil and energy content of the hull-less variety is much greater than ordinary oats. Storage costs are lower, so it is well suited for some speciality food markets. However, yields are lower and because the skin coat is thinner, the oats can be damaged during combining, leading to rancidity problems in storage and reduced shelf life. About 90% of US oats are grown for livestock feed and industrial uses.

ROLL ME AN OAT, PLEASE

Oats get their distinctive flavour from being roasted after harvesting and cleaning. Since hulling the oats doesn't strip away their bran and germ, they retain the concentration of fibre and nutrients. Over the years they have been milled in different ways. Old-fashioned oats have a flatter shape that is the result of their being steamed and then rolled. You can find out a lot more about processed oats in later sections, but you should be aware that many instant oat products don't have the same beneficial qualities as more natural ones.

THE HISTORY BEHIND A BOWL OF PORRIDGE

SUPERGRASS

10,000 years ago people first started to collect grains. By the end of the last ice age, Man was better organised and had the technology to challenge changes to the environment. Rainfall distribution and sea level changes led to a greater use of grasses and three major groups of cereals were collected, then cultivated, in different parts of the world. Neolithic farmers cultivated oats along with other crops. They used various types of grains and meals stewed in water to form a thick porridge-like dish.

CEREAL THRILLER

In Europe, India and the Near East wheat, barley and oats predominated, although evidence has also been found of oat cultivation in Chinese civilisations thousands of years ago. The oldest oat grains found have been dated to the 12th dynasty in Egypt. The ancient Greeks also made a type of porridge from oats but, as it was not considered an important food source, used it in medicines. Hippocrates, the father of medicine, recommended oats after acute fevers and in convalescence.

Even then oats were counted as a sure way of fortifying the body and the Romans knew all about their qualities, too. Talking about oat bread, Pliny the Elder (c. AD 23–79) apparently said, 'This bread, from which we live, contains almost countless remedies.' The Romans also used oats, however, as an important source of nutrition for its armies, marching across Europe. They also introduced the scythe for harvesting cereals, straw and hay crops. The straw retained enough nutrition to double up as hay for cattle in times of need. The husks were easier to remove after burning, and from toasted grains people produced pastes by mixing the crushed, toasted grain with water to form a sort of dumpling. This could be eaten without baking and was quick to prepare. Toasting made the grain digestible. Grain pastes were a major part of the diet of the poor through Roman times, especially in cities where the hazard of fire prevented many people from cooking in their homes.

China and South East Asia cultivated mainly millet and rice, which thrived on the climate. In Central America wild forms of maize were developed. This type of regional cultivation accounts for the reason why today porridge is made from a variety of cereals. Wherever people lived and communities evolved, flat grinding stones, or saddle querns have been found. These were needed to process the hard grains to make porridge or flour.

WHAT'S BREWING?

The Anglo Saxons made porridge from rye, barley and oats and their tribes probably introduced porridge to Britain. This porridge, called 'briw', was served either plain or with vegetables added. These included cabbage, parsnips and carrots, which were introduced by the Romans. Some porridges were fermented, so perhaps that's where we get the word for a brew. It must have been quite difficult to prevent fermentation taking place, since storage conditions would have been somewhat haphazard. A warm moist spell could wreak havoc with cereals.

Porridges were easy to cook and had an advantage over bread: you didn't need to have an oven or grind grains to make flour; you only had to crack the grains and cook them in a pot on the edge of a fire.

TOP CROP

By 1086, twenty years after the Battle of Hastings and the start of the Norman Conquest, 80% of all the land which would eventually be farmed by 1914 was already in agricultural use. The survey of land use carried out for the Domesday Book recorded that 35% of land was under arable use and 25% was pasture. Landowners were rich and the population was growing fast. Land was mostly cultivated on a rotation of two to three years. In 1100, arable crops would be grown for up to ten years without a fallow break, rendering the soil fairly infertile. Peas and beans were grown which acted as a fertiliser for cereal crops and, although wheat grown as the main bread crop and rye was popular in dry areas of the country, oats remained widespread throughout the uplands and on less fertile soil. Barley was grown for malt and brewing.

Fertility was measured by the number of ploughs per square mile, with areas of Sussex and Hertfordshire leading the table with four ploughs. Poorer areas, such as the north and the Somerset levels, recorded only one. *The Domesday Book* also records 6000 mills in operation for grinding grain, all of which were water mills. It was not until the 12th century that windmills were introduced to Britain.

A STEW BY ANY OTHER NAME

In medieval times cooking took place over a fire which was constantly fed. The diet of mostly vegetables and grains with a little meat was usually stewed over the fire, with leftovers remaining in the pot overnight. You can imagine the build up of bacteria over time, as oatmeal has quite a reputation for harbouring unpleasant micro-organisms. Those on the edge of starvation made use of every scrap, re-cooking the stew for breakfast and adding ingredients when possible. A stew of grains, vegetables, water and bacon scraps became known as 'pottage' (which is very close to the French 'potage', a kind of soup).

When I told my brother I was writing this book, he told me about a midnight foraging trip he undertook whilst camping with a scouts' troop about 40 years ago. He decided he would finish off the porridge from breakfast that nobody had washed up. Unfortunately he was ill all next day, and since he was the only known porridge thief, there was only one conclusion to be reached. Goldilocks must have got off lightly, then! There is probably also some sense to the *Pease porridge hot* rhyme.

WHEAT WITH YOUR MEAT?

From Saxon times a wheat based porridge called frumenty or furmenty was used as an accompaniment for meat or as a breakfast meal. It was made from hulled wheat and meat stock seasoned with spices. Try your powers of translation on this little lot:

Tak clene whete & braye yt wel in a mortar tyl the holes gon of; seethe it til it breste in water.

Nym it vp & lt it cole.

Tak good broth & swete mylk of kyn or of almand & tempere it therwith.

Nym yelkys of eyren rawe & saffroun & cast therto; salt it;

lat it naught boyle after the eyren ben cast therinne.
Messe it forth with venesoun or with fat motoun fresch.
(Original 14th or 15th century English recipe for
frumenty)

The recipe was adapted in Norman times to include milk
and egg yolks. The rich overlords would eat frumenty
with strongly flavoured meats such as game, wild boar or
venison. Later it also formed the basis of many more
dishes, sweetened with honey, fruit, spices or vegetables.

CRUEL NOT COOL!

Gruel was a porridge made of grain, usually rolled oats
and water. It was not a very exciting or nourishing
foodstuff, but a thin concoction of a small handful of
rolled oats to five or six cups of water. Dickens made
good use of gruel as a metaphor for poverty and ill
treatment in the workhouses of Victorian Britain, but
we're getting ahead of ourselves. Gruel could be
sweetened with almond milk. A dish called Gruya was
made in medieval times with barley boiled in flavoured
milk. Burstin was made from ground, roasted barley and

also served with milk; we should remember that sugar was not available to the masses in the eighteenth century.

Water gruel, made from oatmeal and water and flavoured with butter and pepper, was served in the eighteenth century. Rich people ate it with wine, sherry or dried fruit but the poor ate it on its own, for any meal.

GROWING OATS? A PIECE OF CAKE!

Oats became popular as a crop throughout Europe in the Middle Ages because they were easy to cultivate. There is mention from John Gerard in 1597 that:

'Common Otes is used in many countries to make sundry sorts of bread . . . Jannocks, Haver cakes, Tharsse cakes . . . which are called generally Oten cakes . . .' He added: 'These naked Otes immediately, as they bethreshed, without helpe of a Mill, become Otemeale fit for our use . . . Some of those good house-wives that delight not to have anything but from hand to mouth . . . may (whiles their pot doth seeth) go to the barne and rub forth with their hands sufficient for that present time, not willing to provide for tomorrow.'

DOCTOR OATS?

Maybe the movement for whole grain, organic foods was already getting underway in the 16th century, or perhaps it was a way of keeping the women in their place. The rich would not consider eating oats, which was for animal feed and medicinal use. They did use oatmeal for pain relief, apparently, by putting grains of oats into linen bags and heating them:

> *'Common Otes put into a linnen bag, with a little bay salt quilted handsomely for the same purpose, and made hot in a frying pan, and applied very hot, easeth the paine in the side callt eh stitch, or collicke in the belly.'*

So there you have it: the microwavable sack of grains for easing muscle pains isn't new at all, but another recycled idea, made simpler by the use of technology.

Oats made their way to America in the seventeenth century with Scottish New World settlers. Originally they were used there mainly as a cure for stomach ailments, but their popularity as a breakfast cereal grew. The first commercially packaged oats were sold in 1854, but sales increased with the setting up of the Quaker Oats Company in 1901. Incidentally, the owners were not Quakers at all, but the picture on the packaging still gives that impression. Originally the grains were just rolled flat, but they took a long time to cook. Nowadays, since the grain is toasted, hulled, steamed, cut and rolled, it undergoes a lot of processing.

DIG THOSE OATS!

During the Second World War the Ministry of Food, under the enforced regime of rationing, gave advice on how to make the best use of the food that was available. They gave cookery demonstrations, made radio broadcasts and distributed recipe leaflets. One such recipe for a vegetable pie, named after the Minister of Food, Lord Woolton, included oatmeal as a filler and thickener.

Traditionally, many Scots' households used to make porridge once a week and then cool it before storing it in a porridge drawer in the kitchen. This could then be served cold by the 'piece' or slice, or reheated with boiling water to reconstitute and thin it. Fuel was saved in this way, being hard to come by in the city tenements. An alternative was to fry it in a pan as required.

FOOD FOR THOUGHT

Oatmeal was a favoured porridge until the 1950s, when oat production started to decline; it wasn't until the late 1980s that studies revealed oat bran's healthy attributes. The 21st century has seen increased consumer demand for all things oaty: from ready-to-eat oat breakfast foods and traditional porridge to oat biscuits and chewy cereal bars. Recently annual sales of porridge oats have risen to 79 million pounds and appear to be matching sales figures for wheat-based breakfast cereals.

Health statistics may help to explain why Scotland has opened the world's first porridge bar, in Edinburgh. The diet of 15th century city dwellers certainly didn't contain sugary drinks, take-away/fast food, chips, pizza or burgers. Obesity and levels of heart disease were not causing national concern and a shortening of life expectancy. Mind you, people didn't smoke then, either!

HEALTH BENEFITS

For centuries, oat grains have been valued for their significant medicinal properties and benefits for maintaining a healthy body. As early as 400 BC ground oat was used on skin for drying and healing, and early civilisations were certainly aware of its numerous benefits.

Porridge has undergone something of a makeover in recent years, partly due to the popularity of the GI (Glycaemic Index) diet. It is also a good source of complex carbohydrates, which release energy slowly into the bloodstream. As they are wholegrain, oats have the natural goodness that is absent from processed cereals.

UNDERSTANDING THE GLYCAEMIC INDEX

The Glycaemic Index ranks foods based on their effects on blood sugar levels. The lower the rating on the index the better it is for blood sugar levels. Only foods which contain carbohydrates appear on the index. Slowly absorbed foods have a low GI rating, so those that are more quickly absorbed get a higher rating. By choosing foods which are slowly absorbed you help to regulate blood glucose levels. This is particularly important for people who have diabetes, although there are obvious benefits for many other groups as well. The standard reference for a GI food is 100, which is the effect on blood glucose levels of a portion of food containing 50g of carbohydrate over a three hour period, compared with that of glucose or white bread. Previously, people believed that all carbohydrates had the same effects on blood glucose levels, but it is now recognised that different foods containing carbohydrates have different effects on these levels. So 50g of bread does not have the same effect as 50g of pasta.

Meals that include low GI foods allow us to absorb carbohydrates more slowly, thereby helping to maintain even glucose levels in the blood between meals. The effects can carry over into the next meal, thus aiding levels throughout the day. Slow acting foods help reduce peaks in blood glucose that often follow a meal. This can help to prevent or reduce the risk of Type 2 diabetes. The following chart gives some idea of the different values given by various products. Bear in mind that 50g of raw oatmeal is quite a large portion, so it goes a long way!

FOOD	GI	SERVING IN GRAMS	CARB/SERVING IN GRAMS
Porridge made from raw rolled oats in water	42	250	20.3
Traditional porridge oats	51	250	20.3
Instant porridge	65	250	20.3
Stone ground medium oatmeal (raw)	59	50 (dry)	34
Porridge from steel cut oats cooked in water	52	50 (dry)	37.4

WEIGHT LOSS AND FINDING A BALANCE

Low GI foods help to control the appetite by giving you a 'full up' feeling for longer, which means that you eat less.

It is not as easy as it seems to work out the GI of a

meal. You can't just read it off a chart (and immediately feel virtuous), and you can't just confine yourself to a low GI diet because that would give an unbalanced diet. For example, milk and dairy products have a low GI because of their high protein and fat content and chocolate has a medium GI, similarly due to the fat content. Crisps have a lower GI than boiled potatoes. Fat and protein slow down the absorption of carbohydrates, but as with all diets there has to be a balance. It's no good kidding yourself that because chips, fatty food and chocolate are low GI you can eat lots of them, because then you would risk heart disease. Equally, there is no point in cutting out all high GI foods. We need to strike a balance.

Lots of factors affect the GI of a food, as will processing, ripeness of fruit and varieties of vegetables. Pasta and durum wheat, along with oatmeal, have low ratings where whole grains act as a barrier that slows down the absorption of carbohydrates. Beware, however, of thinking that wholemeal bread, where the grains have been ground up, or brown rice will give the same low reading: they are high GI foods. The crucial factor is the addition of whole grain, which is why oats are so good

29

for you. Some mixed grain breads and those with added
oats on are better for you than wholemeal bread.

SOME DRAWBACKS

The index only deals with foods which contain carbohydrates, so is not useful for calculating all of your
dietary needs.

Unfortunately, the GI of a food is not based on
commonly consumed individual portions of foods. For
example, carrots contain only about 7% carbohydrates,
so the portion of carrots you would need to eat to
'achieve' the GI reading would be huge – about 1.5
pounds. Portions of foods like bread, which contain a
higher percentage of carbohydrates, will be smaller,
again reducing the overall GI impact simply because the
index is based on larger measures or portions. Therefore,
if you only refer to the Glycaemic Index, you will end up
overstating the effects of foods containing a small
percentage of carbohydrates. Conversely, the effects of
foods containing a high percentage are likely to be
understated if you use the GI as your only point of
reference. Foods that are mostly water or air will not

cause a surge in your blood sugar levels even if their glycaemic index is high.

This is why scientists developed the idea of glycaemic load. It ranks foods according to actual carbohydrate content (e.g. in a typical portion-size), as opposed to how fast a 50g amount raises blood sugar levels.

GLYCAEMIC LOADS FOR SOME COMMON OAT PRODUCTS

(NB: note the different sized portions.)

NAME OF FOOD	SERVING SIZE IN GRAMS	GL PER SERVING
Scone	25	8
Porridge oats	250	17
Oatbran bread	30	9
Muesli	30	16
Instant porridge	250	17

DIABETES

Porridge oats are high in energy yet low in fat, so a bowl of porridge is one of the best meals to start the day with. Because oats are rich in fibre and carbohydrates they help to stabilise blood sugars, therefore they are invaluable to people suffering from diabetes. Porridge leaves you feeling full for a long time so you don't crave mid-morning snacks, thus staving off mood swings. The trick is to find the right ingredients to go with it so that you don't need added/artificial sweeteners. Having been diagnosed with Type 2 diabetes, I've undertaken some experiments on my breakfast porridge with this in mind.

When I was younger and my mum made us eat porridge on winter mornings, I always found that the best bit was the spoonful of golden syrup we added. Reverting to porridge without the traditional addition of either sugar or salt is something else, and not having either full cream or semi skimmed milk is another obstacle to overcome. Help is at hand. Of course, if you're young, fit, not overweight and don't have to worry about your blood pressure or cholesterol levels: lucky you! Long may it stay that way. You can enjoy – for now – the 'Full Monty' of porridge consumption, complete with all the goodies some of us are denied. Have a drool at the recipes!

SUPERFOOD

Compared with other whole grains, oats have one of the highest concentrations of protein, calcium, iron, magnesium, zinc, copper, manganese, thiamin, folacin and vitamin E on a per gram basis. No wonder porridge is one of the five superfoods recommended by nutritionists and the health lobby! The other four are nuts, broccoli, blueberries and avocados.

Lowering cholesterol, preventing heart disease and strokes

Produced in the liver, cholesterol is a fatty substance used to digest fats. We have two types of cholesterol, one 'bad' and one 'good'. It is also found in beef, poultry and dairy products. When our bodies have more cholesterol than the body can use, the cholesterol levels in our blood rise and can lead to blocked arteries, blood clots, heart attacks and strokes. The cholesterol lowering effect of oatmeal is quite well known, having received huge publicity in the media. Oats are an important source of both soluble (55%) and insoluble (45%) dietary fibre. The soluble fibre, beta-glucan, prevents cholesterol being absorbed into the bloodstream and then carries it out of the body. A diet rich in oats for six weeks has been found to lower both blood pressure and cholesterol. About three grams of soluble fibre a day alongside a low fat diet help to lower cholesterol and prevent heart disease. One portion of oatmeal provides about two grams, so by eating a bowl of porridge for breakfast, you're nearly there already, but don't forget your five portions of fruit and vegetables as well.

A further benefit in the prevention of cardio vascular disease was recently discovered, where antioxidant compounds which are unique to oats were found to prevent damage from free radicals. When vitamin C was added to the oat phenols, the effect was to greatly improve the prevention of arteriosclerosis. So if you were to cut up an orange to eat with your oats, or drink a glass of pure orange juice with your oatmeal, you'd be doing yourself almost twice as much good.

Benefits for post menopausal women

Eating a portion of whole grains such as oats has been found to be especially good for women who have reached the menopause. At least six portions per week are apparently a good idea for treating high blood pressure, high cholesterol or other cardio vascular diseases. One study in Denmark found that women eating the most whole grains, nuts, seeds and berries had higher levels of lignan in their blood, which protects against breast and other hormone-dependent cancers and heart disease. Other studies have also highlighted an increase in sexual pleasure after eating more oats.

Responding to infections

The beta-glucan found in oats helps the body's immune system to fight bacterial infection by helping to locate infected tissue rapidly. This rapid response results in faster clearance of micro-organisms and healing. Again, a bowl of porridge a day will boost your immune system.

Antioxidants and anti-cancer treatment

As well as being high in fibre, oats are a very good

source of selenium, which works with vitamin E in a number of antioxidant systems throughout the body. Selenium also helps decrease asthma symptoms and heart disease, and is associated with a reduced risk of colon cancer and other carcinogens in the gastrointestinal tract. Recent research has found that the benefits from whole grains like oats have been underestimated for a long time. Alongside corn, whole wheat and brown rice, oats provide high levels of phenolics, which are powerful antioxidants.

Regular habits

Insoluble fibres serve as effective laxatives and are thus useful in treating constipation. They have been used in treating diseases of the gall bladder and kidneys and in preventing diarrhoea.

Alternative to wheat for celiac disease

Although celiac disease requires lifelong avoidance of gluten, which is found in wheat, rye, barley and oats, some adult sufferers have shown that oats are tolerated because they contain only a small amount of gluten.

Children treated on a wheat-free diet with some oats for a year were shown to have improved lining of the small bowel, which is damaged by eating wheat gluten. Their immune systems had returned to normal.

Many claims to fame

People suffering from rheumatism have found relief by eating porridge, as have those suffering from a hangover. Among the other benefits claimed for porridge are tackling obesity and aiding pregnancy. They are said to have aphrodisiac properties and are also reputed to regulate thyroid problems.

Oats are included in old remedies for nervous conditions, anxiety and insomnia and they alleviate water retention. Allegedly, eating oats can also help to deal with withdrawal symptoms from giving up smoking tobacco.

Skin conditions

The medicinal qualities of oats derive from all parts of the plant, including the straw, green stems and leaves. Additionally, flours, soups, soaps, oat milk and other preparations can be made from them. Oats have often been used in baths to help skin conditions, have helped burns to heal and can reduce the effects of eczema. (NB. Although generally used as a useful compound in skin care, oats can also trigger skin problems in some people, so always test a small area of skin first). Being rich in silica, oats are also known to help renew bones, skin, nails, hair and other tissue.

Fatigue

Oats are considered to be a very nourishing food to aid recovery from illness or exhaustion. The grains contain sterols and alkaloids which have been found to be beneficial in the reduction of anxiety. Oats have a relaxing and calming effect and are a rich source of iron, manganese and zinc. It's always surprising to see people put a bowl of porridge on their list of comfort foods, although I do agree that hot porridge in the morning gives a feeling of wellbeing. I can't see myself creeping down to make a quick fix of porridge at other times of the day, however. There must be some chemistry I'm missing. Claims have also been made for its long term effects against nervous illnesses, shingles, herpes and chronic depression.

Insomnia

Oat preparations contribute to the good functioning of the thyroid gland and of the entire endocrine system. Similar effects can be produced by mattresses and pillows filled with straw, chaff and oat leaves. A French friend vividly remembers his family being given mattresses filled with oat husks and straw when younger. He recalls sinking into these mattresses and falling asleep, aware of the popping of husks as he drifted off. The down side became apparent when he awoke – he couldn't turn over because he was moulded into the mattress, which then itched as the straw came through the covering. I think I'll pass on the mattress idea, but who knows what the oats could do, hidden in a well padded pillow?

Fertility

From Anglo Saxon times oats have been considered an important contribution to the health and fertility of women. Oats were one of five plants that were considered to restore a woman's fertility, the other plants being ginger, wheat, rose and cress.

It's not only humans who have claimed improvements in fertility and virility from eating oats. Read any farming or livestock journal and you will find advice about improving a bull's condition by extra oats in his diet before allowing him to visit his herd, or, less poetically, before the AI collector calls for the samples. That reminds me of the 'Rent-a-bull' adverts we used to read weekly in our local paper in North Yorkshire.

Horses also receive extra attention on the oats front when stamina is needed. Getting their oats, indeed!

Aphrodisiac qualities

Research has apparently shown that oats have positive effects in reversing or combating not only sterility but also impotence. It is known that oat preparations contribute to the equilibrium of the endocrine and other systems and wild green oats are said to boost the effects of other herbal aphrodisiacs. Oats provide a stimulating effect on the body, and are said to free up bound testosterone: hence the term 'feeling his oats.' They are certainly considered to be good as a restorative tonic, ideal for energy deficiency. I read somewhere that wearing a kilt has quite an effect on male fertility and virility, so perhaps a bowl of oats just adds to the effect!

WORDS OF CAUTION

Oats and Purines

Oats contain naturally-occurring substances called purines, which are commonly found in plants, animals, and humans. In some individuals, excessive intake of these substances can cause health problems. Purines can be broken down to form uric acid, and too much of this can increase the risks related to kidney problems or gout. Sufferers of these conditions may want to limit or avoid foods such as oats.

LITERARY AND CULTURAL CONNECTIONS

Oats and oat based foods have given rise to a whole vocabulary that originated in Scotland, and gradually spread far and wide. First of all, the generic term 'blanter' was used to describe food made from oats: for example oat bread and porridge. You could take a drink of 'blenshaw' with it, if you wished, a concoction of oatmeal, sugar, milk, water and nutmeg. If you came from North Roxburgh and you wanted to serve milk with your porridge you would use your 'luggie': a small wooden bowl with handles formed from projecting staves.

'Brose' is a dish of oat- or pease-meal mixed with boiling water or milk, with salt and butter added, but you'd probably want to avoid it cooling so much that it left you with a 'brat': the crust or coating that forms on the surface of a liquid, such as curdled cream on milk or skin on your porridge. For the strong of stomach, especially in North Perth, a good dose of 'cauld steer(ie)', that is cold 'brose' – oatmeal stirred in cold water or sour milk – would set you up for the day, though, personally, I much prefer the sound of 'crackins', a dish of fried oatmeal, now found in the north-east.

Talking of the north-east, my husband's father, a coalminer from Sunderland who moved to Kent in the 1920s to find work in the newly opened collieries, always talked of the food he took with him to work as his 'snap' (kept securely in a miner's 'snap tin'). This was clearly a reference to 'snap and rattle' or toasted oatcakes crumbled in milk, famous in the north-east.

ANOTHER COUNTRY, ANOTHER NAME

Porridge itself – or the name for it – varies widely even within the confines of Scotland. For instance, the Gaelic word for it is 'lite' (pronounced leetch-yuh). In Shetland they use the word 'milgruel', and the thin porridge made with the liquor in which kale has been cooked is known as 'tartan-purry'. 'Brochan', a thick or thin gruel with, for example, butter and/or honey added, is sometimes considered to be a porridge, especially in Arygll and Ulster.

Rabbie Burns may well have described porridge as

'chief of Scotia's food' in his poem The Cotter's Saturday Night (1786) but its fame and influence have certainly spread well beyond the boundaries of Scotland. The sheer number of different names for porridge dishes tells us what a significant part it plays in the life and culture of nations all around the world. In some countries it has medicinal qualities, helping patients to recuperate. For example, 'rice congee', a type of rice porridge eaten in several Asian countries, especially China, is valued for its therapeutic properties. It is also served in Japan, where it is known as 'kanji'.

Another Japanese porridge dish, called 'okayu', is given to sick people much in the way that chicken noodle soup is offered to ailing citizens in the USA. It is also commonly used by the Japanese to wean their infants onto solid foods. The fact that 'congee' is often served during times of famine underscores its importance as a staple to eke out meagre food supplies and puts us in mind of the place of porridge in the poorhouse, in the hard times of Dickensian England.

The porridge we all know and love in the UK, including 'flummery' (Wales) and 'fuarag' or 'crowdie'

(Scotland), is called 'oatmeal' or 'oatmeal mush' in the United States. It is also a traditional Scandinavian and Icelandic breakfast. In Finland there is a porridge based Christmas food, eaten with cinnamon and sugar, known as 'ruishiutaleita'. In Norway they have 'risgrøt', made with rice and vanilla, cooked with milk and served with cinnamon, sugar and butter; while in Morocco you may come across 'zematur'.

There are several types of maize porridge, such as grits, traditional in the southern United States. In Mexico 'atole' is a warm, porridge-like concoction made with water and milk. In Romania 'mamaliga' is popular, as is 'cornmeal mush' in southern and mid-Atlantic US states. In Italy 'polentina', which can be made from corn or barley, also contains raisins, milk and sugar. In southern India the traditional 'uppama' or 'uppma', a fried semolina ('suzi' or 'shuji') porridge, is flavoured with clarified butter, fried onions, toasted mustard seeds and curry leaves. It is also often mixed with vegetables and potatoes, fried red chillies, fried cauliflower and toasted peanuts or cashew nuts.

FOOD FOR THOUGHT

So many varieties of both names and dishes, and we haven't even mentioned 'peasemeal' (or 'pease'/'pea') porridge, buckwheat porridge mixed with yoghurt, popular in Russian ethnic areas and in the Caucasus region or 'quinoa' porridge (ground quinoa flakes mixed with cocoa or cinnamon) from ancient Mayan culture. Not to mention millet porridge, much favoured in the Middle East and often seasoned with cumin and honey, and, last but not least, rye porridge. No wonder Spike Milligan felt moved to campaign for a permanent reminder to us all of its enduring status in his poem simply entitled 'Porridge'.

Ian Dury and the Blockheads also considered porridge to be one of their 'Reasons to be Cheerful', but their view was not shared by other creative artists. Despite the enthusiasm of Messrs Milligan and Dury, porridge has not always been a cause for celebration. Dr Johnson, in the first comprehensive English dictionary published in 1747, sarcastically dismissed oats as:

> *'a grain, which in England is generally given to horses, but in Scotland appears to support the people.'*

Fortunately, the entry did not go unchallenged since John Boswell, a writer from north of the border with England, offered the following trenchant riposte:

> 'Which is why England is known for its horses and Scotland for its men.'

WHAT THE DICKENS . . . ?

Charles Dickens's alternative term for porridge – 'gruel' – could hardly be more fitting, given the circumstances to which his characters inevitably find themselves reduced. Impoverished, without friends and family and shamelessly exploited by an appallingly cruel society, they find themselves feeling so hungry they long for extra helpings of the most disgustingly unappetising food imaginable: a bowl of porridge.

> *Into these bowls, Mrs Squeers, assisted by the hungry servant, poured a brown composition, which looked like diluted pincushions without the covers, and was called porridge. A minute wedge of brown bread was inserted in each bowl, and when they had eaten their porridge by means of the bread, the boys ate the bread itself, and*

*had finished their breakfast; whereupon Mr Squeers said,
in a solemn voice, 'For what we have received, may the
Lord make us truly thankful!' — and went away to his
own.*

(*Nicholas Nickelby* at Dotheboys Hall, following
brimstone and treacle 'physiking' of new pupils).

Even when Nicholas enjoys slightly improved fortune, he
still gorges himself on the stuff simply to fend off
starvation:

*Nicholas distended his stomach with a bowl of porridge,
for much the same reason which induces some savages to
swallow earth — lest they should be inconveniently
hungry when there is nothing to eat. Having further
disposed of a slice of bread and butter, allotted to him
in virtue of his office, he sat himself down, to wait for
school-time.*

'PLEASE SIR, I WANT SOME MORE, SIR.'

In *Oliver Twist*, porridge — or the relative lack of it —

threatens to become the cause of even murder and cannibalism, leading to one of the most famous literary moments of all time:

The room in which the boys were fed, was a large stone hall, with a copper at one end: out of which the master, dressed in an apron for the purpose, and assisted by one or two women, ladled the gruel at meal-times. Of this festive composition each boy had one porringer, and no more — except on occasions of great public rejoicing, when he had two ounces and a quarter of bread besides. The bowls never wanted washing. The boys polished them with their spoons till they shone again; and when they had performed this operation (which never took very long, the spoons being nearly as large as the bowls), they would sit staring at the copper, with such eager eyes, as if they could have devoured the very bricks of which it was composed; employing themselves, meanwhile, in sucking their fingers most assiduously, with the view of catching up any stray splashes of gruel that might have been cast thereon. Boys have generally excellent appetites. Oliver Twist and his companions suffered the tortures of slow starvation for three months: at last they got so voracious and wild with hunger, that one boy, who was tall for his age, and hadn't been used to that sort of thing (for his father had kept a small cook-shop), hinted darkly to his companions, that unless he had another basin of gruel per diem, he was afraid he might some night happen to eat the boy who slept next him, who happened to be a weakly youth of tender age. He had a wild, hungry eye; and they implicitly believed him. A council was held; lots were cast who should walk up to the master after supper that evening, and ask for more; and it fell to Oliver Twist.

THE BARD AND THE BOWL

Shakespeare was no stranger to the attributes of porridge and made reference to it throughout his works. In *Macbeth* Banquo uses it as a potent symbol of personal matters, in which, he claims, he would never dream of meddling, declaring: 'I never thrust my nose in other men's porridge.' The cynical, sarcastic Sebastian, in *The Tempest*, uses the term to conjure up an admittedly repellent image ('cold porridge') with which he mocks

Alonso, who is trying to be positive about their misfortune in being stranded on a remote island following the shipwreck:

ALONSO: *Prithee, peace.*
SEBASTIAN: [Apart to Antonio] *He receives comfort like cold porridge.*

Since porridge could also be made from peas ('peace') Sebastian no doubt thought his pun about porridge was both clever and witty. In *The Tragedy of King Lear*, Edgar, posing as Tom, a demented beggar (the name 'Tom' was common amongst beggars at the time) tells Lear of his supposed woes and enemies, and how his own particular demon (the 'foul fiend') has tormented him, even trying to poison his porridge:

KING LEAR: *Didst thou give all to thy two daughters?*
And art thou come to this?

EDGAR: *Who gives any thing to poor Tom? whom the foul fiend*
hath led through fire and through flame, and through

sword and whirlpool o'er bog and quagmire; that hath laid knives under his pillow, and halters in his pew; set ratsbane by his porridge;

ONE MAN'S PORRIDGE . . .

Ironically, Jean-Jacques Rousseau (1712–1778), a French philosopher and writer who believed in the natural goodness of man (whom he felt was warped by society) and whose work influenced the theories of the French Revolution and the Romantics, felt his enemies kept trying to poison his porridge when he visited Scotland. He also deserves credit for his promotion of vegetarianism thanks to his support for natural foods, including porridge. As he said in Emile:

One of the proofs that the taste of flesh is not natural to man is the indifference which children exhibit for that sort of meat, and the preference they all give to vegetable foods, such as milk-porridge, pastry, fruits, etc.

Some people, of course, need no persuading that porridge on its own (and, no doubt, Scottish cuisine, for those wanting to show their hatred of all things Scottish) is poison enough: for Ronnie Barker, in the richly comic series of the same name, porridge – also known, with obvious connections, as 'stir' – was something imposed on you, in this case a stretch in prison. Scots should feel free to dismiss this as mere culinary racism on the part of the English or 'sassenachs' (an ancient derogatory term for a Saxon), who should know better, as was clearly the case with Cosmo Gordon Lang, Archbishop of Canterbury from 1928 to 1942; he once infamously remarked to his audience in Edinburgh, 'If you take the shorter catechism, the psalms, and Sir Walter Scott, and mix them with porridge, you will breed a great race of men.'

STAND UP FOR PORRIDGE!

Porridge is the subject of numerous superstitions and legends. Talking of 'stir', there are those who insist that porridge should be stirred in a clockwise direction using the right hand to avoid invoking the devil. This stirring should be done with a straight wooden spoon without a moulded or flat end, known as a 'spurtle' or 'theevil'. Curiously, you should also always refer to porridge as 'they' and, according to custom, you should eat it with a bone spoon whilst standing up.

Quite recently, HM Prisons finally decided to stop offering porridge to inmates for breakfast; as an economy measure, they have replaced it with individual boxes of cereal and a third of a pint of milk, placed inside prisoners' cells before the previous night's lock-up. Although porridge is clearly not as popular as it was in prisons, there are surely still some who rue the passing of the institution – the homely, warming comfort of an early morning bowl. For old lags it is even more serious than that; according to one of their superstitions, on the day of their release from prison, they should eat a large bowl of porridge – if they fail to finish it off, the story goes, they will inevitably be forced to return to prison to finish it, while they are doing another stretch!

A (MING) VASE FULL OF PORRIDGE?

According to legend, Zhu Yuanzhang, a man of lowly birth who became the first emperor of the Ming Dynasty (1368–1644), was the founding father of the '8th

December Porridge Festival'. Allegedly, on December 8th the young Zhu and some of his hungry friends cooked up a porridge from some rice, corn and beans they had found stored for winter in a mousehole in a field. Years later Zhu led his poor people in the uprising that overthrew the emperor and saw Zhu installed in his place. The banquet of coarse cereal porridge he held on December 8th each year, to remind him of his humble origins and of the time when he had tasted the most delicious food ever, gave rise to today's '8th December Porridge Festival' of Tianjin, a city that once served as a stronghold for Beijing.

FASCINATING FACTS

NORSE NOUS

In the age of the Vikings porridge was not only cooked
to provide nourishment for hungry explorers,
marauders and pillagers. The metalwork of their cooking
utensils, in particular their cooking pots, often left gaps
through which food, liquids and, of course, valuable heat
could be lost during cooking. Therefore, the canny
Vikings worked out a cunning plan to seal their pots for
more efficient and economical mealtimes.

They cooked up either fruit or porridge in the
unsealed pot and allowed the boiling contents to ooze
through the gapped metalwork. Once on the outside of
the pot, the boiling fruit or porridge would soon burn
and coat the outer surface, thus closing the offending
breaches. All that then remained to be done was to clean
the inside of the pot before cooking anything else in it.
Yum, yum, Erik!

TOPPING UP THE POT

People in North America in the 1500s often cooked in

the kitchen in a big kettle hung over the fire. Every day they lit the fire and added things to the pot to make a stew consisting mainly of vegetables, as there wasn't a lot of meat to be had. Any leftovers would remain in the pot to go cold overnight and then be used to start a 'fresh' stew the following day — not the healthiest of diets, as the stew could end up having food in it that had been in there for a month. This doubtless gave rise to the chant, 'Peas porridge hot, peas porridge cold, peas porridge in the pot nine days old.'

THICK SKIN, THIN SKIN

The asphodel plant, like oats, is versatile, not only as a source of food but also for its medicinal applications. As far back as the 4th century, Theophrastus explained how the asphodel stem could be fried, the seed toasted and the root chopped and eaten with figs. When used to treat skin conditions, particularly those caused by over-exposure to sun or harsh weather, it eases irritation and softens and refreshes. Porridge made from fresh asphodel roots has also been used to lighten freckles.

THE PORRIDGE POT – CRATER MASS?

If you saw a photograph of the Porridge Pot – a swirling, bubbling, mud volcano in New Zealand – you'd understand immediately how it got its name. Since it is created by hot spring activity, with lots of sulphurous gas and small amounts of water reacting chemically with surrounding rock, you'd probably also be able to conjure up the appalling, acrid smell, too. Oats may well be associated with beauty care, but this particular porridge pot wouldn't guarantee you the finest of mud to apply as a face pack – unless you fancy a complexion like the surface of Mercury!

DEVIL'S PORRIDGE

The Devil's Porridge exhibition tells the story of HM Factory in Gretna, described as 'the greatest munitions factory on earth'. In 1915, Britain was losing the First World War, through acute lack of ammunition. The war effort was transformed by the arrival of 30,000 women and men from all over the world, who came to work in the massive munitions factory on the Solway, where cordite production rapidly outstripped that of all the other munitions factories in Britain combined.

Sir Arthur Conan Doyle, creator of the immortal detective, Sherlock Holmes, coined the term 'devil's porridge', when he visited the factory, in 1918. There he found the workers mixing by hand a curious, highly explosive paste, a mixture of nitro-glycerine and nitro-cotton. Once dried, the paste was processed into cordite, making it look like uncooked spaghetti. This potent concoction was then put into artillery shells and bullets to propel them, delivering quick, hot bursts of energy to the enemy.

PORRIDGE POT ALLEY

The name 'Porridge Pot' is highly popular – you will come across hundreds of restaurants and pubs within and beyond the British Isles bearing the name. There is even a road called 'Porridge Pot Alley' in London. I wonder if it's related to 'Tin Pan Alley'?

THE GOLDEN SPURTLE

If you were to journey to Inverness-shire in October you might be in for a surprise. No, there wouldn't be a teddy bears' picnic to greet you, but Goldilocks herself would be hard pressed not to find a dish to her taste. Carrbridge is the venue for the World Porridge Making Championships, held in conjunction with the Highland Food and Drink Festival, or Highland Feast.

In recent years this has become more of an international event, with interest spreading across the globe. Connoisseurs travel to the event to compete for the coveted Golden Spurtle, along with other prizes. Recipes for the perfect porridge, along with a range of other ingredients, are tried and tested by judges in different categories.

The spurtle itself is a long-handled implement resembling on first inspection a thin rounders bat or truncheon. Spurtles have been in existence since at least the 16th century. There are two types: one spatula type for turning oatcakes and scones, the second a tapered stick for stirring porridge. A closer look obviously shows marked differences not apparent from an initial impression. Spurtles are also known as theevils or theedles in localised areas of Scotland. They were used before the introduction of rolled oats, when the oatmeal needed more time for softening and therefore required a longer cooking time. The use of a spurtle prevented the formation of large, stodgy lumps, like the sort I got when I first tried to cook medium oatmeal in a microwave without frequently stirring it. That particular consignment went in the bin.

Spurtle Etiquette

Various traditions survive in some quarters, whereby the whole process of making successful porridge and consuming it rely on certain procedures and what could be described as old wives' tales. But who can be sure which is which? I'll let you decide.

Stirring 'widdershins' is said to invoke the devil or bring bad luck. You should always stir 'deiseal', that is sunwise or clockwise. Use of the left hand for stirring is equally bad news. This tradition obviously goes back to the days of witch hunts and the idea of left handed people being sinister (from the Latin 'sinister', meaning left). Interestingly, that would not have prevented my late, left handed mother-in-law from stirring the porridge in her native Scotland. She was forced as a child at school in Glasgow to use her right hand for writing and other tasks and became fairly competent with both, if not completely ambidextrous.

Addition of salt too early in the porridge-making process hardens the grain. This prevents swelling and results in a less creamy bowl of porridge. Ah well, on a low salt diet, I'll just have to put up with cooking it a bit longer, or settle for second best.

The traditional way of referring to porridge is 'they' and 'they' should be stirred with a spurtle, rather than a spoon.

Eat 'them' at the table, standing up. This possibly originates from when oats were eaten as whole grains, which must have weighed heavily on the stomach. Several accounts, ancient and modern, suggest that this tradition still survives.

COOKING WITH OATS

Now that you're convinced that oats are an essential part of a balanced diet and really do you good, here are a few general uses and ways of sliding them into dishes for the non-porridge-eating members of the family.

- I've been slipping them into crumble toppings as a matter of course for years, and it's amazing how even the most sceptical of palates don't seem to complain. They usually ask what the nutty taste is. Adding a few flaked almonds for disguise is a further ruse I've been known to use.
- You can replace up to one third of the flour in most recipes with oats or oat flour. Oats help retain moisture.

- Replace breadcrumbs with oats when making meatballs or meatloaf.
- Use ground oats instead of breadcrumbs, or as a mix, for fish or poultry.
- Use oats in stuffing.
- Add a handful to soup and stew recipes.

DID YOU KNOW?

Oats have a slightly higher fat content than other grains, and so it's best not to purchase huge quantities as they go rancid quicker. They are cheap enough to buy regularly and in addition you can freeze oats or store them in an airtight container. It's best to store them in a cool, dry, dark place. Properly stored oats will last for several months.

Oats are also used in salad dressings, sauce thickeners, ice-cream coatings and stabilizers, baby foods, beverages, baked goods and snack foods. Oat starch is slow to crystallize, so it is stable from freezing to thawing and holds up well under high temperatures.

PORRIDGE RECIPES

There seem to be as many ways to make your bowl of porridge as there are days in the year. I don't propose to bore you with them all, but try a few of my favourites.

Traditional porridge for two

80 g (4 tbsp) medium oatmeal.
450 ml (¾ pint) water
150 ml (¼ pint) milk
½ tsp salt
1 tbsp cream (optional)

- Place the salt, water and milk in a medium saucepan. Sprinkle in the oatmeal, stirring all the time, and bring to the boil.
- Turn it down to simmer and stir continuously for 10–15 minutes. The mixture will bubble and thicken, so keep stirring to make sure no lumps form.
- Remove from the heat and stir in the tbsp of cream if you are indulging yourself.
- Serve with brown sugar, honey or treacle, or sweet fruits.

Traditional Scottish porridge recipe

1 cup oatmeal
3 cups of water
1½ cups milk
Knob of butter
½ tsp of salt

• Put oatmeal, water and milk in a pan, stirring all the time.
• Bring to the boil, add butter and salt.
• Keep stirring until it thickens.

Old fashioned baked porridge

You could serve this as a dessert, topped with ice cream. This amount serves two. Although the sweet ingredients have been cut by half, they still look a bit much to me!

575 ml (1 pint) water
¼ tsp salt
80 g (3 oz) medium oatmeal
25 g (1 oz) raisins

15 g (1 tbsp) maple syrup
15 g (1 tbsp) black treacle
15 g (1 tbsp) dark brown sugar
15 g (1 tbsp) walnuts, chopped
1 egg, beaten
¼ teaspoon cinnamon
¼ teaspoon ground ginger
A pinch of nutmeg
Chilled milk or cream

- Heat the oven to 180°C.
- Bring the water to the boil, add salt, reduce heat and sprinkle in the oats.
- Cook for 5 minutes, stirring frequently.
- Transfer the oatmeal to an ovenproof dish. Add all the remaining ingredients, (except the milk or cream). Stir well.
- Bake until set (approximately 40–45 minutes).
- Spoon into bowls and serve with milk or cream.

Three grain porridge

A hot cereal, perfect for cold mornings. It serves two, but may need planning ahead because of the cooking time. Serve with milk and honey and add sliced bananas for extra luxury. It certainly needs something to mop up all that goodness! Served with soya milk it would be suitable for vegans.

700 ml (1¼ pints) water
80 g (3 oz) rolled oats
80 g (3 oz) rice
80 g (3 oz) barley

- Bring the water to the boil.
- Add the grains, lower the heat and simmer for about 45 minutes, stirring occasionally.

Orange and ginger porridge

The only difference to this recipe might be to leave out the caraway seeds, which are a bit of an acquired taste, especially first thing in the morning.

120 g (8 tbsp) porridge oats
²⁄₃ tsp ground ginger
½ tsp caraway seeds (optional)
4 tsp sugar or artificial sweetener
3 tsp low-fat yoghurt, crème fraiche or single cream
700 ml (1¼ pints) water
2 tsp chunky marmalade mixed with 2 tsp boiling water
  for a topping

- Mix the porridge oats, water, ground ginger and
  caraway seeds in a saucepan and bring to the boil.
- Simmer and stir until thickened.
- Add sugar or sweetener.
- Pour into bowls and top with yoghurt or crème fraiche
  and the marmalade mixture.

Golden porridge with fruit crust

The topping is adaptable to whatever fruits and nuts you want.
I think it sounds good as an alternative topping for a fruit
crumble as well, avoiding the use of fats.

YOU WILL NEED FOR THE PORRIDGE:

½ tsp salt

80 g (3 oz) medium oatmeal

575 ml (1 pint) water

1 tbsp treacle

1 tbsp honey

½ tsp cinnamon

YOU WILL NEED FOR THE CRUNCH TOPPING:

1 tbsp dried currants

1 tbsp dried cranberries

1 tbsp flaked almonds

1½ tbsp sugar

2 tbsp oatmeal

- Prepare the topping first by roasting the oatmeal in a dry frying pan, stirring all the time until it goes brown. Add the other topping ingredients and continue to stir.
- Put water, salt and oats in a pan and bring to the boil. Simmer and stir for about three minutes.
- Add the milk, treacle, honey and cinnamon and continue to cook, stirring constantly for another three minutes, or until thickened.

• Serve hot, sprinkled with crunch topping.

You could prepare the crunch topping in advance, especially if you are using the oven. In this case, spread the ingredients out on baking paper and roast for about ten minutes until golden. This can be stored in an airtight container until needed.

Steel-cut oat porridge with pineapple

Steel-cut oats are much grittier than porridge oats, so give a firmer texture. You could substitute the pineapple for raisins or mixed dried fruit.

150 g (5.5 oz) steel cut oats
320 ml (just over ½ pint) water
1 dessertspoon black treacle
1 tsp brown sugar
40 g (1½ oz) crushed pineapple with juice
½ tsp cinnamon

• Boil the water and sprinkle in the oats and brown sugar.

- Reduce heat and simmer.
- Stir in pineapple, juice, treacle and cinnamon.
- Simmer for 20 minutes, stirring occasionally and adding additional water if necessary to prevent sticking. Cook until the oats are soft.

Baby bear's porridge that was just right

80 g (3 oz) porridge oats, or quick cook oats
pinch salt
575 ml (1 pint) milk
½ banana
40 g (1½ oz) chopped walnuts or raisins
2 tbsp flaked coconut or 2 tbsp brown sugar

- Cook the oats in the milk with salt or according to package directions.
- Place in serving dishes.
- Peel the banana and cut into thin slices. Arrange these on top of the porridge. Add the walnuts or raisins.
- Sprinkle coconut or brown sugar on top of porridge.
- Serve with extra milk, if necessary.

Blueberries and cream porridge

80 g (3 oz) oatmeal
575 ml (1 pint) water
150 g (5–6 oz) blueberries
Pinch of cinnamon
40 ml evaporated milk (optional)

- Bring the water to the boil in a small saucepan. Add the oatmeal and cook, stirring until thickened.
- Add the blueberries and cinnamon. Just before serving, add the evaporated milk.

Luxury caramel porridge

This recipe suggests the old method of soaking oats overnight. Most other aspects are more modern in approach. The original recipe required making caramelised milk, as for banoffee pie, but a much simpler solution is to buy caramel cream from the supermarket.

1½ cups porridge oats
1½ cups water
1 vanilla pod (opened)

2 extra cups water
Pinch of salt
30 ml (2 tbsp) caramel cream
1 tot butterscotch liqueur (or other, to taste)

- Soak the porridge oats overnight in the water and vanilla.
- Next day cook the porridge with the extra water and salt.
- Stir in the caramel cream and tot of liqueur.
- Serve with mini marshmallows and double cream.

OTHER BREAKFAST RECIPES

Home-made granola

For the uninitiated, granola is the US equivalent of muesli. The basic ingredients are oats, nuts and honey, baked until crispy and then mixed with raisins or dates. The idea is that you prepare a batch of granola and use it as a breakfast food or snack to eat when doing something active and healthy, like hiking or camping. You can eat it with milk as a cereal or poured over yoghurt to give texture and flavour. It is lightweight, high in energy and easy to carry. Over the years the added ingredients have made it into something closer to junk food, with marshmallow, chocolate, peanut butter, and hydrogenated fats. Because there is no flour, however, or oil, granolas are high in fibre, if high in sugar as well.

225 g (8oz) porridge oats
80 g (3 oz) flaked almonds
80 g (3 oz) raisins
80 g (3 oz) cashew nuts
60 g (2 oz) desiccated coconut
2 tbsp brown sugar
2 tbsp maple syrup or honey
2 dessertspoons vegetable oil

- Mix the oats, nuts, coconut and brown sugar in a large bowl.
- Combine maple syrup and oil and add to the dry mix.
- Mix well and pour onto 2 baking sheets.
- Cook for 75 minutes in a very cool oven (130°C, 250°F, gas mark just 1). Stir every 15 minutes or so to make the mix brown evenly.

- Remove from the tins to a large bowl and mix in the raisins. When cool the mix can be stored in a biscuit tin, plastic bag or screw top jar.

Oats and fruit breakfast mix

You may find it convenient to prepare your oatmeal up to a month ahead. In this recipe, you mix together the dry ingredients and just microwave a cupful at a time. I don't know if it will save time in the mornings. I like to choose what to mix into my porridge on a daily basis.

400 g (14 oz) porridge oats
30 g (1 oz) raisins
30 g (1 oz) dried fruit
1 tbsp brown sugar
1 tsp cinnamon
Pinch of salt

- Combine the first 7 ingredients and store in an airtight container.
- In a deep microwave-proof bowl, put ½ cup of porridge mix and 1½ cups of water.

- Microwave on high for one minute and stir.
- Cook for a further 30–60 seconds or until thickened.
- Let it stand for one to two minutes before eating.

Luxury muesli

150 g (5½ oz) porridge oats or jumbo oats
1 tbsp demerara sugar
1 tbsp chopped, roasted nuts
1 medium apple, cored and chopped
1 banana sliced
150 ml (¼ pint) milk
Lemon juice (optional)

- Mix the dry ingredients.
- Dip the fruit into lemon juice if you want to prevent browning.
- Pour the milk over and allow to stand for 10 minutes. to soften the oats slightly before eating.

MAIN COURSE RECIPES

Herrings in oatmeal

This is a classic way to cook fresh herrings, and it's also doubly healthy because of the fish oils. When mackerel are plentiful and cheap you could use them instead.

4 herrings, cleaned and gutted
60–80 g (2–3 oz) fine oatmeal
50 g (2 oz) butter or margarine
Lemon wedges for serving
Salt and freshly ground white pepper

- Season the herrings and press them into the oatmeal on the skin and flesh side, brushing off any excess oats.
- Heat the butter in a heavy frying pan and cook the herrings for 4–5 minutes on each side until golden.
- Serve with lemon wedges and preferably with boiled, new potatoes.

Roast guinea fowl (or chicken) with haggis and oat stuffing

Haggis, mixed with extra oats makes a good stuffing for game and poultry. You don't often see guinea fowl on special offer in the supermarket, but this works equally well for chicken: either one larger bird or two small ones.

FOR 2–4 SERVINGS:

2 guinea fowl, each weighing about a kilo
500 g (1 lb) haggis
1 tbsp oats
2 tbsp chopped parsley
Knob of butter
Salt and freshly ground black pepper
1 onion, quartered
2 carrots, cut into chunks
½ tbsp flour
500 ml (1 pint) chicken stock
1 tbsp whisky (optional)

• Pre-heat the oven to 230°C (450°F, gas mark 8).
• Mix the haggis, oats and parsley together and push the

79

stuffing into the cavities of the guinea fowl or the chicken.

- Put the vegetables into a roasting tray, rub the fowl with butter and season well. Place the fowl on the vegetables, breasts facing up and cook for 15 minutes.
- Turn the oven down to 200°C (400°F, gas mark 6) and continue cooking for 40 minutes, basting occasionally. If you have one larger bird you will need to adjust the cooking time accordingly, to ensure the stuffing is cooked properly.
- Transfer the fowl onto a heated plate and surround it with the vegetables.
- Put the roasting tray on a low heat on the stove top. Stir the flour into the juices and gradually add the whisky and stock, stirring well. Simmer for about 5 minutes, until the sauce has thickened.

Golden oats pork chop casserole

Tasty pork chops on a bed of oats, onions, apple, orange and herbs.

4 pork chops
1 tbsp cooking oil
2 onions
2 eating apples, diced
1 orange, peeled and sliced
Pinch of thyme
Salt and pepper
25 g (1 oz) butter or margarine
175 g (6 oz) porridge oats, uncooked
1 egg
100 ml (4 fl oz) water or broth

- Combine the oats and egg in a bowl and mix until the oats are thoroughly coated.
- Trim any excess fat from the chops and sprinkle with pepper. Brown on both sides in oil.
- Remove chops from the pan and cook the onion in the same pan with the butter or margarine.

- Add the oats mixture to the onions, stirring constantly until lightly browned.
- Add the water, salt, diced apple, orange, thyme and continue cooking, stirring occasionally until the liquid evaporates.
- Transfer to a casserole dish and arrange the chops on top. Cover and bake at 180°C (350°F, gas mark 4) for about 45 minutes.

Meatloaf with oats

Oats make a perfect substitute for breadcrumbs. Using minced chicken or turkey makes an excellent substitute for beef, and for the last year I've only used turkey mince for meat loaf, lasagna or pasta sauces. Most people don't notice the difference. Turkey mince is virtually fat-free, very cheap to buy and it means the whole family can eat the same thing. I often line the tin with a couple of strips of bacon, making it a lot more salty, but very popular with everyone else.

500 g (1 lb) beef or turkey mince
3 tbsp ketchup, or
2 tbsp tomato puree

150 g (5 oz) oats
1 onion, finely chopped
1 tbsp parsley
½ teaspoon paprika
2 sliced back bacon (optional)

- Mix all ingredients together in a large bowl.
- Line a loaf tin with bacon, or grease the tin.
- Pack in the meat mix and bake at 180°C (350°F, gas mark 4) for 45 minutes–1 hour.
- Turn out onto a plate to serve, with seasonal vegetables.

Spicy Prawns with oatmeal butter

I can feel my cholesterol rising at the thought of this recipe, and even the oats won't do too much good, being of the quick cook variety. However, it sounds interesting, if you can eat what you like.

SERVES 2:
300 g (10½ oz) cooked prawns
45 g (1½ oz) butter or margarine
3 egg yolks, beaten lightly

1 tbsp chopped garlic
1 tbsp shallots
1 tsp instant chicken bouillon granules
½ tsp sugar
Pinch of curry
2 hot chilli peppers (or to taste)
Salt and pepper, to taste
75 g (3 oz) quick cook oatmeal

- Sauté egg yolks in the butter or margarine and add garlic, chicken stock granules, sugar, curry leaves, chillies, salt and pepper.
- Continue to fry till fragrant. Add the prawns and stir.
- Lastly, add the oatmeal and fry until dry. Serve hot.

Root vegetable crumble

For this recipe you can use any seasonal root vegetables, or add a slightly more exotic feel by using sweet potatoes, plantain and even more spices. Don't worry if you haven't got all of the root vegetables: this is just a guide.

SERVES 6:

2 onions, peeled and roughly chopped
2 cloves of garlic, peeled and crushed
1 tsp thyme
1 tsp cumin seeds
50 g (2 oz) butter or margarine
1 tbsp flour
1 litre (2 pints) vegetable stock
1 parsnip, peeled and cut into 2 cm (1 in) chunks
1 small swede, diced
2 carrots, diced
2 turnips, diced
Salt and freshly ground black pepper
½ celeriac root, diced

FOR THE CRUST:
60 g (2 oz) butter or margarine
60 g (2 oz) breadcrumbs
2 tbsp grated, mature cheese
60 g (2 oz) porridge oats
2 tbsp chopped parsley

- Pre-heat the oven to 200°C (400°F, gas mark 6).
- On the hob gently cook the onion, garlic, thyme and cumin in the butter or margarine until soft.
- Add the flour and stir well, gradually pouring in the vegetable stock a little at a time to prevent lumps forming. Add the vegetables, season and simmer for 20–25 minutes, until the vegetables are tender. There should be just enough sauce left to bind the vegetables, if not turn the heat up to reduce it a little.
- Meanwhile make the crust. Mix the breadcrumbs, oatmeal and parsley with melted butter or margarine. Pre-heat the oven to 200°C (400°F, gas mark 6).
- Transfer the vegetables to an oven-proof dish and spoon on the topping to cover the vegetables. Top with grated cheese and bake for 30–40 minutes, until golden.

Speedy Oatmeal Burgers

These meatless burgers are quick and easy.

MAKES 4 BURGERS:

225 g (8 oz) oatmeal
½ tsp salt
1 tsp sage
1 medium onion, chopped
3 eggs
1 can reduced fat cream soup, eg tomato or asparagus
300 ml (10 fl oz) water

- Mix the oatmeal, salt, and sage and then add the chopped onion and eggs.
- Drop large spoonfuls onto a hot non-stick frying pan. Brown on both sides.
- Mix soup and water, pour over burgers. Cover and simmer on low heat for 20 minutes.

Cheese and onion oat flan

I love this combination of cheese and onion, although there's a lot of fat, what with the cheese, milk and margarine. Using skimmed milk will keep down the fat, and you could use a low fat cheese, as long as it doesn't taste like soap. Still, the oats will do you good!

120 g (4 oz) wholemeal flour
120 g (4 oz) oatmeal
120 g (4 oz) margarine
Water for mixing
Pinch of salt
2 eggs
3 chopped onions
150 ml (¼ pint) skimmed milk
225 g (8 oz) grated cheese of your choice
Pepper

• Put the flour, salt and oatmeal into a large bowl and rub in the margarine.
• Add enough water to mix to a firm dough.

- Turn onto a floured surface, knead and roll out to line a flan dish.
- Put in the fridge while you make the filling.
- Heat some oil in a pan to fry the chopped onions. Fry until they start to turn brown.
- Beat the eggs and add the milk, then the onions and most of the cheese.
- Put into the pastry crust, add the rest of the cheese and a good pinch or grinding of pepper.
- Bake at 190°C (375°F, gas mark 5) for 35–40 minutes.

FOR THOSE WITH A SWEET TOOTH

Honey flapjacks

200 g (7 oz) butter
200 g (7 oz) demerara sugar
200 g (7 oz) honey
400 g (14 oz) porridge oats
50 g (1¼ oz) nuts, dried fruits, glacé cherries, chopped
 or desiccated coconut (optional)

- Heat the butter, sugar and honey until the sugar has dissolved.
- Add the oats and nuts, fruit, or coconut and mix well.
- Place in a greased swiss roll tin or cake tin and spread to about 2 cm (¾ in) thick.
- Bake in a preheated oven at 180°C (350°F, gas mark 4) for 15–20 minutes, until golden around the edges, but soft in the middle. Let it cool in the tin, then turn out and cut into squares.

Oatcakes

These simple oatcakes are easy to make and very good for you.
They can be served with butter, low fat cream cheese or hummus.
If you prefer, use a cutter to make individual oatcakes.

350 g (12 oz) fine oatmeal
1 tsp salt
150 ml (¼ pint) boiling water
40 g (1½ oz) soft margarine
Pinch bicarbonate of soda

- Put the oats, salt, and bicarbonate of soda into a large bowl.
- Melt the margarine in water over a low heat.
- Add to the oats and mix to a dough.
- Turn out onto sprinkled oatmeal and knead until you have a smooth dough.
- Dust a rolling pin with oatmeal and halve the dough roll out into two 25 cm (10 in) rounds.
- Cut into 8 sections and place on greased baking sheets.
- Bake in a cool oven 150°C (300°F, gas mark 2) for 1 hour until crisp. Cool on a wire rack.

Oatmeal muffins

Surprisingly tasty without any spices or flavourings. The oats need to soak for 1 hour before preparing the recipe.

MAKES 12 MUFFINS

225 g (8 oz) porridge oats
225 ml (8 fl oz) buttermilk or skimmed milk
1 egg
125 g (4 oz) brown sugar
125 g (4 oz) soft margarine, melted
225 g (8 oz) plain flour
1/2 tsp salt
1 tsp baking powder
1/2 tsp bicarbonate of soda

- Soak the oats in the milk for 1 hour.
- Add beaten egg and mix well.
- Add sugar and melted margarine, mixing well.
- Fold in sifted flour, baking powder and bicarbonate of soda.
- Bake in greased tins or papers at 200°C (400°F, gas mark 6) for 15–20 minutes.

Oatmeal caramelitas

This sounds a bit complicated, so read through the whole recipe before you start. It involves partially cooking then adding caramel milk topping mixed with flour as a sandwich layer in the middle before completing the process.

MAKES 10–12 BARS

300 g (11 oz) plain flour
75 g (2½ oz) plain flour
300 g (11 oz) oatmeal
225 g (8 oz) brown sugar
½ tsp baking soda
½ tsp salt
225 g (8 oz) butter or margarine, melted
225 g (8 oz) chocolate chips
150 g (5 oz) chopped walnuts
⅔ jar caramel topping

- Preheat oven to 180°C (350°F, gas mark 4). Grease a swiss roll tin or baking dish.
- Combine the main quantity of flour, oats, brown sugar, baking soda, salt and butter in a large bowl.

- Press half the mixture into the bottom of the baking dish and bake for 10 minutes.
- Sprinkle chocolate chips and walnuts over the base.
- Mix the caramel topping with the rest of the flour and mix well. Pour this over the chocolate chips and nuts.
- Sprinkle the remaining oat mixture evenly over the base and bake for about 20 minutes.
- Cool completely before cutting into bars.

Peanut butter and oatmeal no-bake cookies

These no-bake cookies are certainly low in fat, if rather high in sugar. I think reducing the sugar might be a good idea.

700 g (24 oz) oatmeal
75 g (2½ oz) low fat peanut butter
10 ml (1 dessertspoon) vanilla essence
450 g (16 oz) brown sugar
120 ml skimmed milk
60 g (2 oz) butter

- Mix the oats, peanut butter and vanilla.

- Put the sugar, milk and butter in a saucepan. Heat gently until ingredients are melted, then boil for one minute.
- Pour over the oatmeal mixture and stir rapidly.
- Place heaped tablespoons onto plates or trays and leave to cool and set.

Chocolate oat bites

100 g (4 oz) soft margarine
50 g (2 oz) brown sugar
3 tbsp golden syrup
175 g (6 oz) porridge oats
50 g (2 oz) chocolate drops

- Cream the margarine and sugar together.
- Add the golden syrup, oats and chocolate. Stir thoroughly.
- Put the mix into a greased cake tin and smooth the top with a spoon.
- Bake at 200°C (400°F, gas mark 6) for 20 minutes.
- Leave in the tin to cool and then cut into bars or slices.

Broonie

Fine oatmeal gives this mild gingerbread a texture like wholemeal bread. Try eating it warm.

175 g (6 oz) fine oatmeal
175 g (6 oz) plain flour
60 g (2 oz) butter or margarine
1 egg
1 tsp ground ginger
2 tbsp treacle
1 tsp baking soda
150 ml (¼ pint) milk

- Sift the flour, ginger and baking soda and mix with the oatmeal.
- Melt the butter or margarine with the treacle and add to the oat mix.
- Stir well and add the egg, well beaten.
- Gradually stir in the milk.
- Pour into a greased loaf tin and bake at 200°C (400°F, gas mark 6) for 60–80 minutes. It should be well risen and firm on top.